Let's Go,
Crew!

Jake leads his mateys on adventures!

Captain Hook tries to spoil their fun!

Izzy has a pouch of pixie dust.

Cubby is part of Jake's crew.

Mr. Smee is Hook's first mate.

Bones and Sharky sing pirate songs.

Connect the dots to find out who sends goose bumps down Captain Hook's spine.

Answer: Tic Toc Croc

Help Skully fly to the treasure. Which line leads him there?

A   B   C

Your Answer:

The Never Land Pirates are having a dance party!

The music reaches the Jolly Roger.

© Disney

Match the letters with the symbols to decode the message.

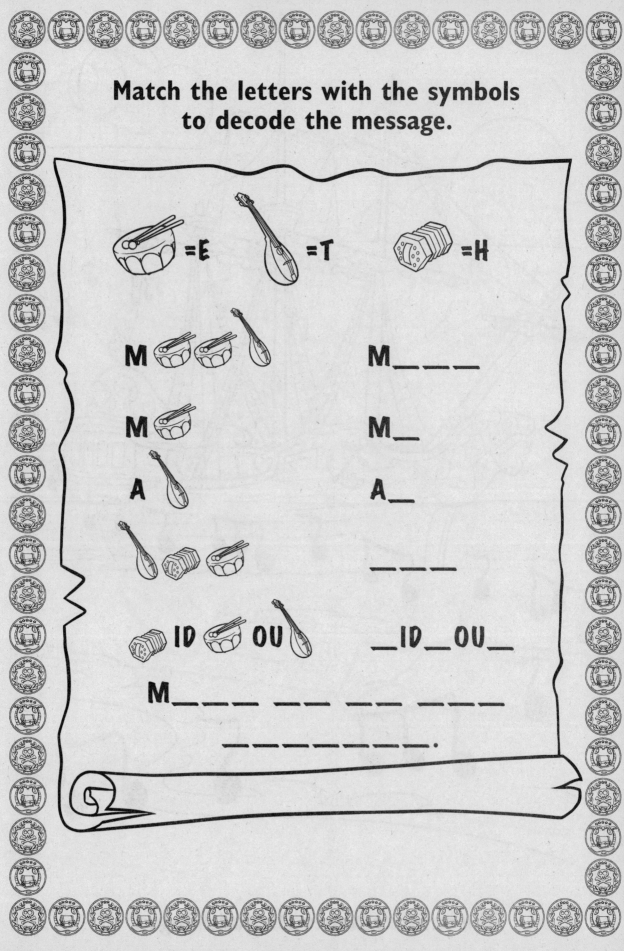

M____

M_

A_

___

_ID__OU_

M____ __ __ ___

_____.

Mr. Smee dances to the beat.

"Mister Smee! Who's making that rat-a-tat racket?"

"It's the sea pups, Captain. They're dancing!"

**Captain Hook spots the happy
crew through his spyglass.**

"This is an outrage," says Hook.
"We must put an end to their fun!"

Which Skully is different?

A

B

C

D

Your Answer: ☐

Answer: B

Use the grid to draw Smee.

"Excuse me. May I join your little party?"

"Ahoy, Captain Hook."

Color 3 pictures of Captain Hook and circle 4 pirate flags.

Go, Cubby, go!

"Great playing, Cubby! You earned 3 Gold Doubloons!"

How many words can you make using the letters in:

DANCE PARTY

_____   _____

_____   _____

_____   _____

_____   _____

_____   _____

_____   _____

"My, my. What fun bangy things!"

"Run, Smee!" cries Captain Hook.

Read the clues and guess who's being described. Circle every third letter in the box to see if you're right!

1. The fairies gave me something very special.

I am _ _ _ _ _ .

```
a e i g
h z p q
z t b y
```

2. Squawk! I'm a great lookout!

I am _ _ _ _ _ _ _ .

```
b j s m n k
o e u w z l
p x l r n y
```

3. Any treasure I see must be mine!

I am _ _ _ _ _ _ _
_ _ _ _ .

```
r w c c h a w t
p k s t p f a a
e i g q n z l h r
w o b n o t t k
```

4. My ship's name is Bucky. Yo ho!

I am _ _ _ _ _ .

```
z m j u
o a k w
k v x e
```

Answer: 1. Izzy, 2. Skully, 3. Captain Hook, 4. Jake

"We can't let Hook spoil our fun.
Yo ho, let's go!"

© Disney

"Look alive, crew!"

Earn 2 Gold Doubloons by finding Hook's exact shadow.

A

B

C

Your Answer: ☐

Find and circle the words.

```
D S E U S D
B E A C H A
B A R O I N
I J L M P C
P I R A T E
K X Q A C F
```

BEACH DANCE PIRATE
SEA SHIP

Follow the clues to solve the crossword puzzle.

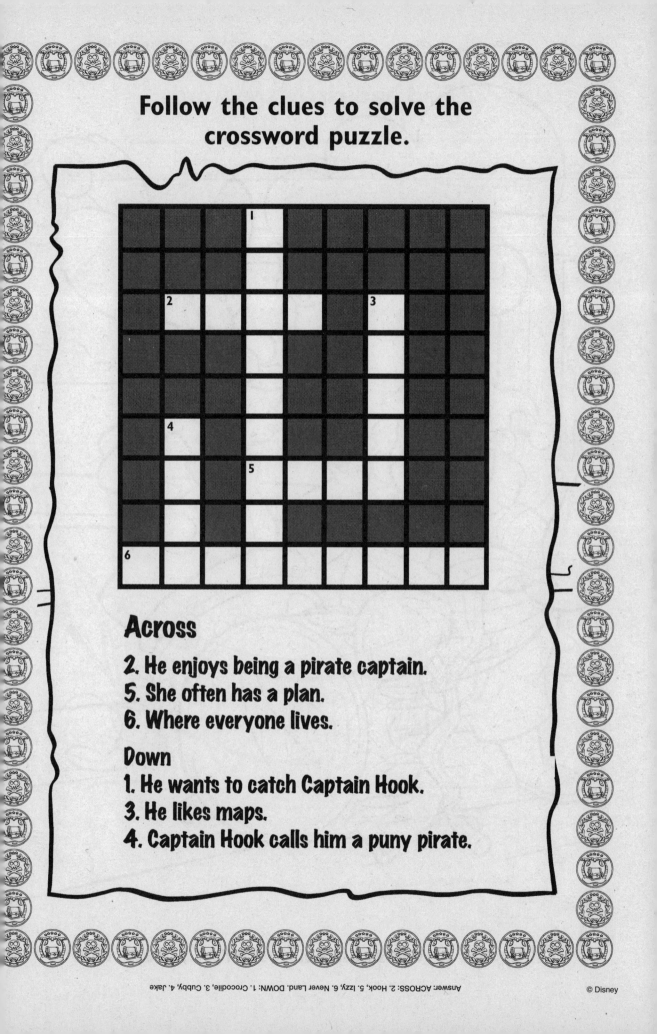

Across

2. He enjoys being a pirate captain.
5. She often has a plan.
6. Where everyone lives.

Down

1. He wants to catch Captain Hook.
3. He likes maps.
4. Captain Hook calls him a puny pirate.

"Play me a waltz, Smee," orders Captain Hook.

Match the pirates to their special items.

"Stop!" yells Hook. "That crashing
and clanging is too much!"

Sharky and Bones sing—
"Captain's plan was a terrible curse,
But ol' Smee's drumming was even worse!"

© Disney

Which pieces complete the picture?

A

B

C

D

E

Your Answers:

 &

© Disney

Connect the dots to complete the picture of Bucky.

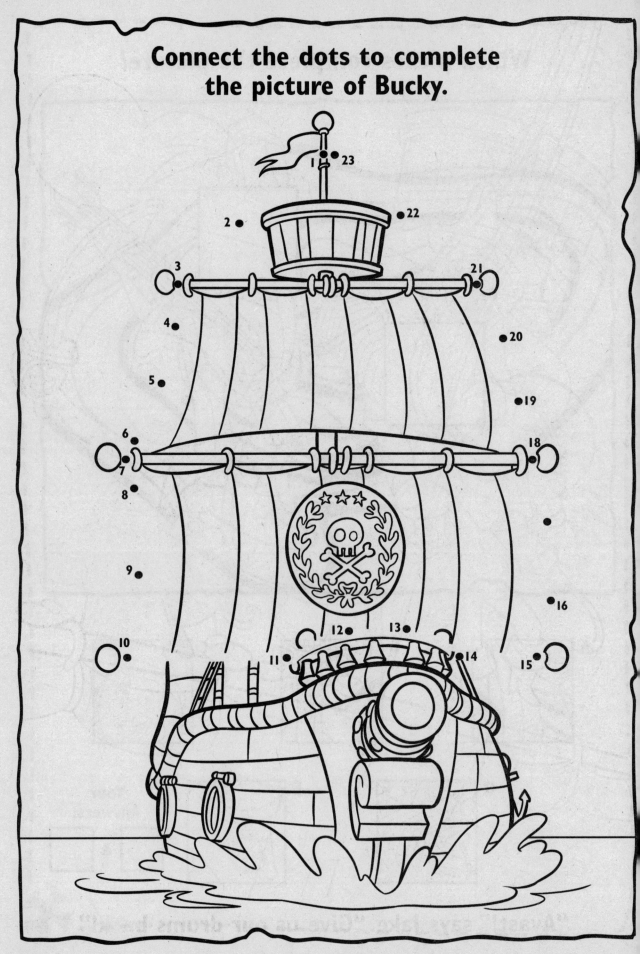

"Avast!" says Jake. "Give us our drums back!"

How many anchors do you count?

Your Answer:

"Grab those pesky pirates!" shouts Hook.

© Disney

"We need a pinch of pixie dust!"

**"We got our drums and earned 3 Gold Doubloons!
Let's grab 'em and go!"**

© Disney

Which pieces complete the picture?

A

B

C

D

E

Your Answers:

[ ] & [ ]

© Disney

Which treasure chest is different?

There are 19 Gold Doubloons already in the Treasure Chest. Count the Gold Doubloons earned and add them to the chest.

Add the number of
Gold Doubloons from above.

$$19 \atop +\underline{}$$

Write your answer here.
Yo ho, way to go!

$=\underline{}$

Yo Ho,
Let's Go!

Look what washed ashore!

"It's an underwater diving helmet!" says Izzy.

How many pictures of each can you find?

Jake: ☐

Skully: ☐

Treasure Chest: ☐

Answers: Jake: 5, Skully: 7, Treasure chest: 4.

Think of words that start with the letters in Bones's name. Two have been done for you.

	Name	Food	Animal	Place
B				
O	OTIS			
N			NARWHAL	
E				
S				

Connect the dots to complete the map of Never Land.

"I spy treasure!" says Captain Hook. "I want to spoil their fun, so I must have that hat-buckety thing."

Look up, down, across, and diagonally for these Never Land words.

JAKE	HOOK	SKULLY
IZZY	SMEE	BUCKY
CUBBY	GOLD	MAP

G	B	U	C	K	Y
O	H	A	B	L	B
L	O	C	L	Y	B
D	O	U	P	Z	U
E	K	A	J	Z	C
S	M	E	E	I	Y

How many letters did you **not** use to find the words?

Circle that many Gold Doubloons.
Let's grab 'em and go!

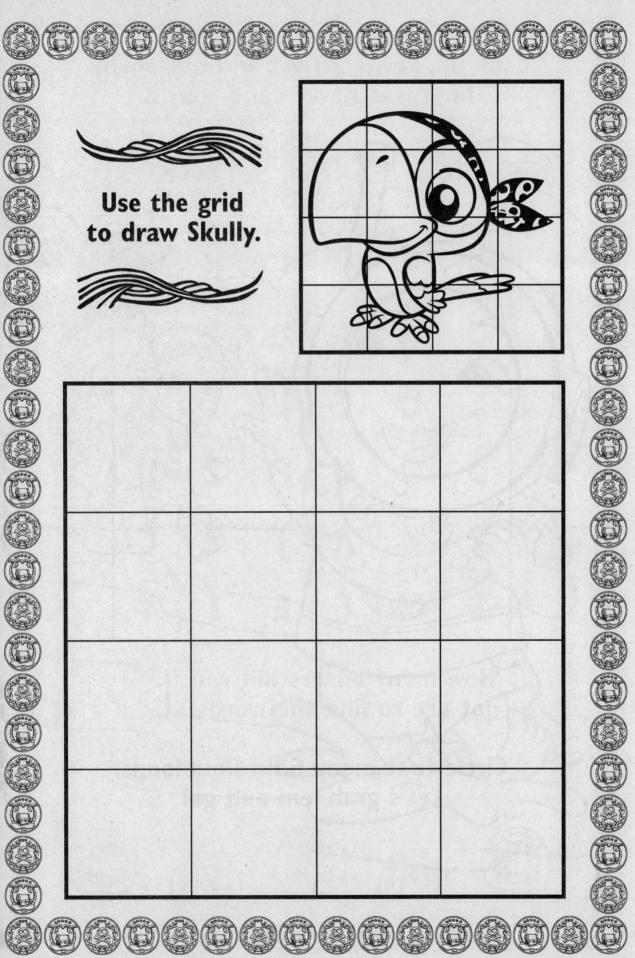

Use the grid to draw Skully.

Cubby is going to look at the fish.

Cubby walks under the water.

**Hanging out
with some friends?
Play a few games
of tic-tac-toe!**

Extreme Close-Up! Can you help Jake figure out who's in the pictures?

A

B

C

D

Which fish is different?

Your
Answer: ☐

Answer: C

"Aha! I've got it! The treasure is mine!"

Can you help Skully
find the skull key
to return it to Jake
and his friends?

FINISH

Look at all those Gold Coins! How many can Smee and Captain Hook gather? Find out by playing this game for two.

Player #1 (Smee) draws a line to connect two dots. (You can draw up and down, or across, but not diagonally.) Then Player #2 (Captain Hook) connects two dots. At some point, a player will connect two dots that will complete a square. Yay! That player puts a S (if player is Smee) or an C (Captain Hook) inside the square, and then gets to take another turn. When all the dots are connected, the game is over. Squares with Gold Coins are worth one bonus point each. The competitor with the highest score is the winner.

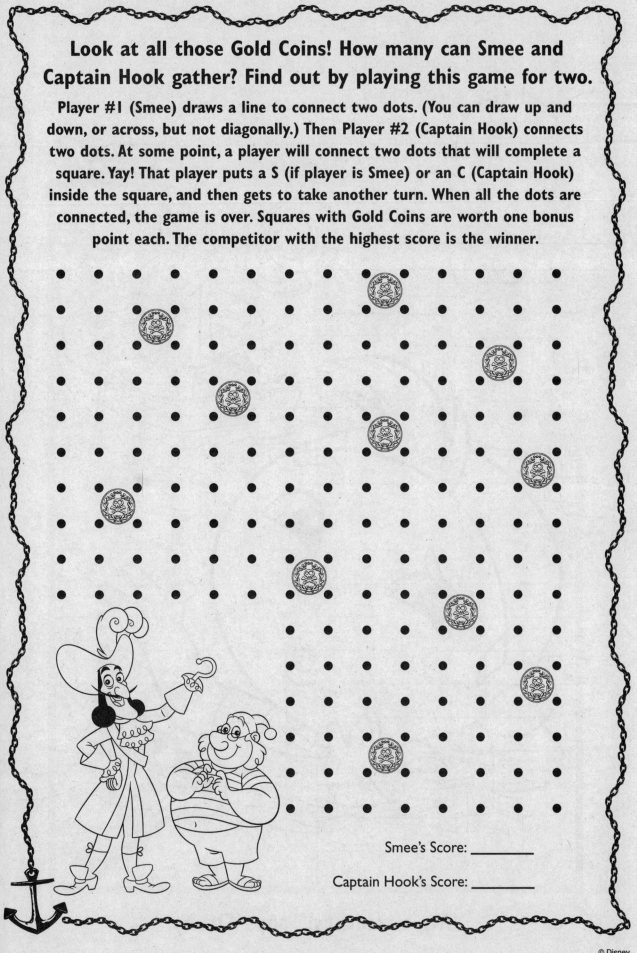

Smee's Score: _____

Captain Hook's Score: _____

© Disney

"Aw, coconuts!" says Cubby.

"The scallywags are headed for Seahorse Shallows!"
squawks Skully.

© Disney

How many pictures of Jake do you count?

Your Answer:

© Disney

Answer: 8

Jake has lost Skully! Which line leads him to his friend?

A   **B**   **C**

Your Answer:

Write the location of the pictures on the grid as shown.

is at **B. 4**   is at __, __   is at __, __

is at __, __   is at __, __   is at __, __

"Let's go, crew!"

Match Jake to his exact shadow.

A

B

C

Your Answer:

Use the key to discover the secret message.

skull & crossbones	G
compass	S
spyglass	E
coin with skull	H
ship's wheel	L
coin with treasure	Y
anchor	T
pirate skull	O

    ,

,

Captain Hook is underwater looking at the seahorses.

**Bucky can't get close to the shore.
The water is too shallow.**

How many seahorses are swimming with Captain Hook?

Your Answer: ☐

Draw lines to match
the characters with their names.

A

❶HOOK

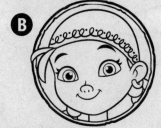
B

❷JAKE

C

❸SMEE

D

❹IZZY

E

❺SKULLY

F

❻CUBBY

"Follow me, mateys!" yells Izzy.
They swing on ropes off the ship to the beach.

"We solved a Pirate Problem by getting to the beach
and got 4 Gold Doubloons! Let's grab 'em and go!"

Jake loves to swing on vines. Draw a picture of something you love.

Help the pirates find their separate ways to get the anchors to the ship.

START

START

START

FINISH

© Disney

"I'm keeping the hat-bucket thingy!" says Hook.

© Disney

Why does Captain Hook
want to keep the hat-bucket thingy?
Use the code to find out.

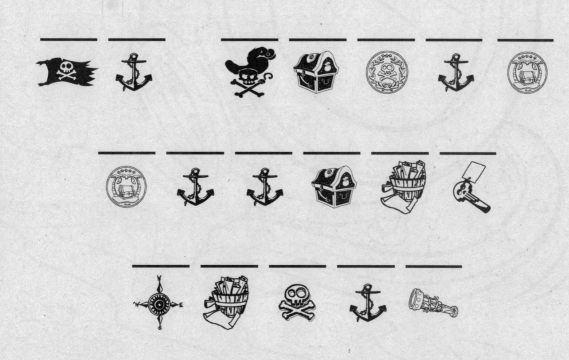

**Skully grabs the helmet.
"Cheese and crackers! I've got it!"**

**"Great work, Skully! We got 2 Gold Doubloons!
Let's grab 'em and go!"**

© Disney

Which two rows of faces are exactly alike?

Your Answers:

[ ] & [ ]

Match Izzy to
her exact shadow.

A

B

C

Your Answer: ☐

Can you follow the clues to solve the crossword puzzle?

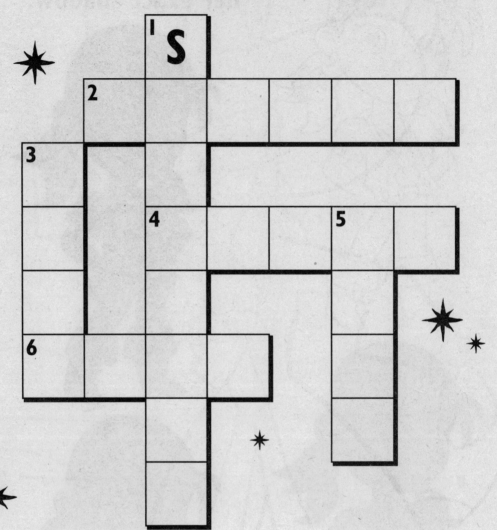

ACROSS:

2. Jake and his crew find a diving _____ .
4. Hook wants to _____ their fun.
6. _____ steals the helmet!

DOWN:

1. Another word for beach is _____ .
3. Cubby saw _____ under the water.
5. _____ swings on a rope to the shore.

Answer:ACROSS: 2. helmet, 4. spoil, 6. Hook. DOWN: 1. Seashore, 3. fish, 5. Izzy

"Barnacles!"

How many words can you think of that rhyme with:

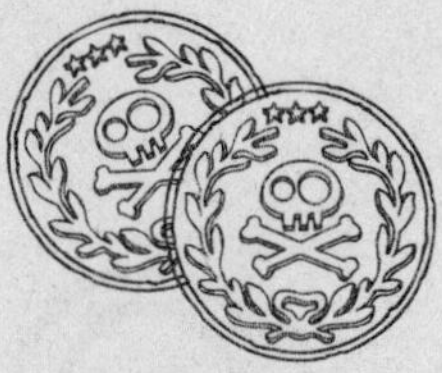

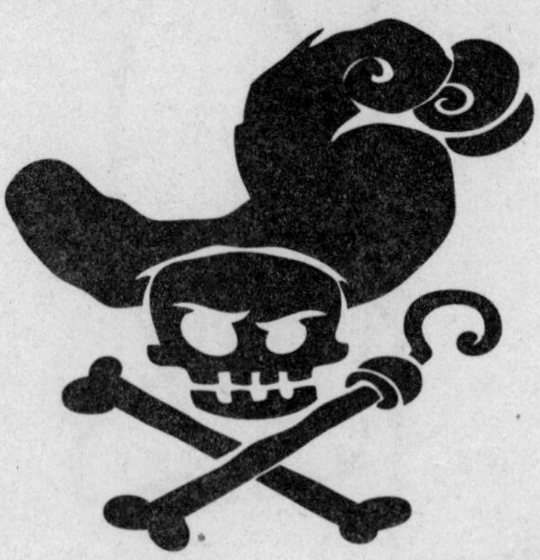

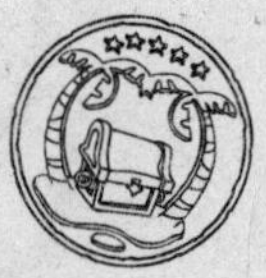

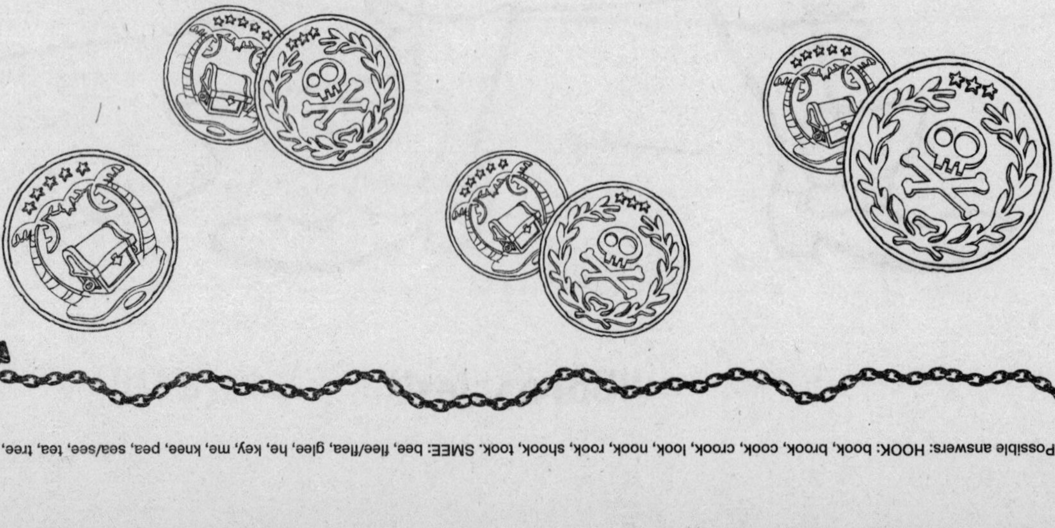

HOOK   SMEE

_____   _____

_____   _____

_____   _____

_____   _____

_____   _____

_____

"This is all your fault, Smee!" says Hook.

"Back to Pirate Island, me hearties!"

Help Jake put the Gold Doubloons in the Team Treasure Chest.

START

How many
do you count?

© Disney

Look up, down, across, and diagonally. Help Jake and the gang find these pirate words!

GOLD
HOOK
SHIP
FISH
ANCHOR

```
A R F I S H T C I T G
Y N C D A P U R S N O
T J C A D H A R L Q L
P P A H D L O G T I D
M I E C O T M O C G E
Z H L B K R L L K J N
H S T I O B D E E G P
```

There are many things
to put in a chest.
Help Jake choose what to put
in his treasure chest by
drawing the next item
in the pattern.

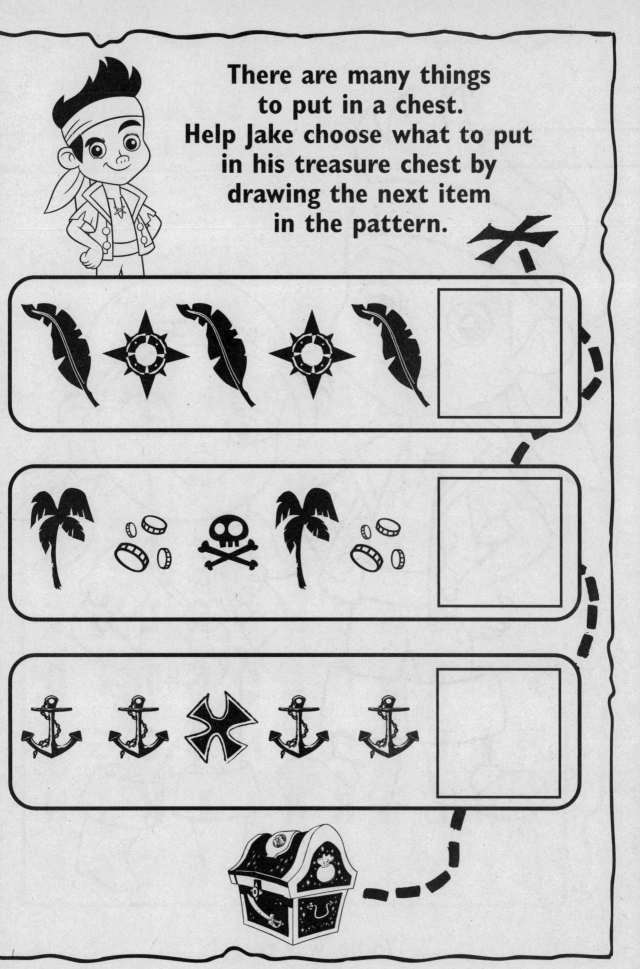

Yo ho, way to go!